CGP

Mental Maths

Key Stage 1
For ages 5-7

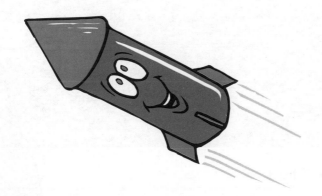

Practise & Learn

Published by CGP

Editors:
Jane Ellingham
Camilla Simson
Rebecca Tate

Updated by Rob Harrison and Ben Train

With thanks to David Ryan for the proofreading.

ISBN: 978 1 84762 962 3

Printed by Elanders Ltd, Newcastle upon Tyne
Clipart from Corel®

Photocopying this book is not permitted. Extra copies are available from CGP with next day delivery.
0800 1712 712 • www.cgpbooks.co.uk

Contents

Adding

When you add two numbers together you get a bigger number. Here's an example.

2 + 3 = **5**   9 + 3 = **12**

Count the objects and add them together.

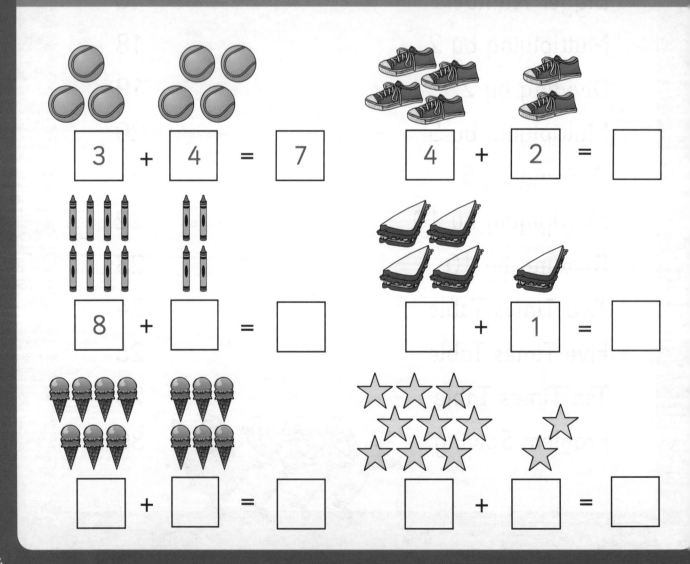

3 + 4 = 7   4 + 2 = ☐

8 + ☐ = ☐   ☐ + 1 = ☐

☐ + ☐ = ☐   ☐ + ☐ = ☐

Add the skittles together and write
the missing numbers in the boxes.

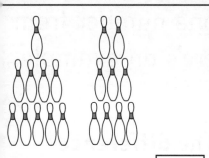
10 + 9 = 19

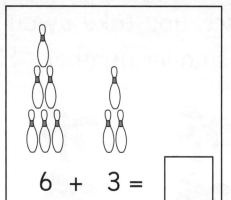
6 + 3 =

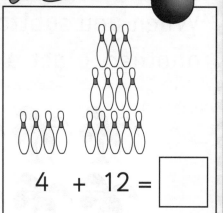
4 + 12 =

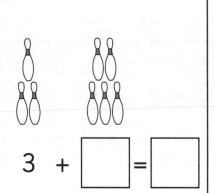
3 + ☐ = ☐

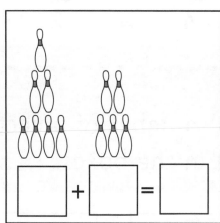
☐ + ☐ = ☐

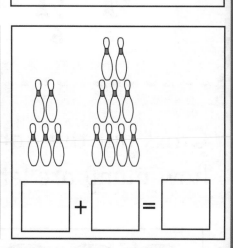
☐ + ☐ = ☐

Add these numbers together and
write the answers in the boxes.

4 + 5 = 9

6 + 2 =

1 + 8 =

7 + 4 =

5 + 8 =

4 + 9 =

15 + 3 =

12 + 7 =

11 + 6 =

2 + 1 + 7 =

3 + 8 + 4 =

6 + 2 + 9 =

Subtracting

When you subtract, you take away one number from another to get a smaller number. Here's an example.

6 − 4 = 2

The **difference** between **6** and **4** is **2**.

Cross out the right number of objects and write how many are left in the boxes.

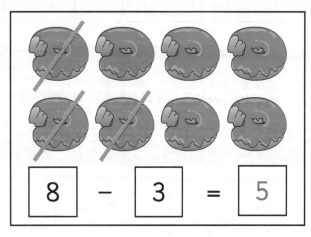

8 − 3 = 5

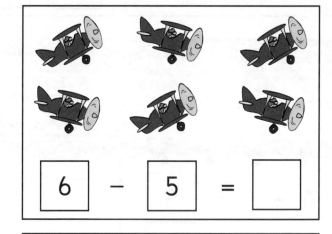

6 − 5 =

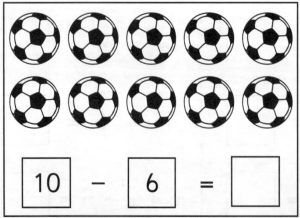

10 − 6 =

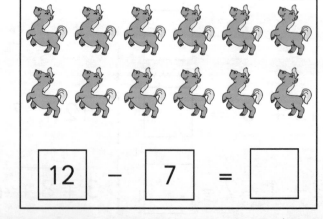

12 − 7 =

6

Work out the answers to the questions and write your answers in the boxes.

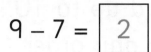

9 – 7 = ☐ 2   10 – 4 = ☐

19 – 15 = ☐   12 – 1 = ☐

8 – 5 = ☐   16 – 8 = ☐

What is 14 take away 4? ☐

What is the difference between six and thirteen? ☐

What is 3 less than 11? ☐

Fill in the boxes to complete the calculations below.

9						15	–		4	=			
–						–						–	
14	–	2	=	12				3				3	
=		–				=			=			=	
						–	9	=				8	
		=											
		2	–	1	=								

Number Facts to 10

Learn the pairs of numbers that add up to 10.
Numbers can be added together in any order.

10 + 0 = 10	8 + 2 = 10	6 + 4 = 10
0 + 10 = 10	2 + 8 = 10	4 + 6 = 10
9 + 1 = 10	7 + 3 = 10	5 + 5 = 10
1 + 9 = 10	3 + 7 = 10	

Draw lines so that each pair of boats adds up to 10.

Learn the numbers that subtract from 10.

10 – 0 = 10	10 – 4 = 6	10 – 8 = 2
10 – 1 = 9	10 – 5 = 5	10 – 9 = 1
10 – 2 = 8	10 – 6 = 4	10 – 10 = 0
10 – 3 = 7	10 – 7 = 3	

Draw lines to match each calculation with its correct answer.

9　　2　　7　　8　　4

| 10 – 3 | 10 – 6 | 10 – 9 | 10 – 8 |

| 10 – 1 | 10 – 0 | 10 – 2 |

| 10 – 7 | 10 – 4 | 10 – 5 | 10 – 10 |

6　　10　　3　　0　　1　　5

Number Facts to 20

Learn the pairs of numbers that add up to 20.

20 + 0 = 20	3 + 17 = 20	13 + 7 = 20
0 + 20 = 20	16 + 4 = 20	7 + 13 = 20
19 + 1 = 20	4 + 16 = 20	12 + 8 = 20
1 + 19 = 20	15 + 5 = 20	8 + 12 = 20
18 + 2 = 20	5 + 15 = 20	11 + 9 = 20
2 + 18 = 20	14 + 6 = 20	9 + 11 = 20
17 + 3 = 20	6 + 14 = 20	10 + 10 = 20

Make all the lines on the star add up to 20.

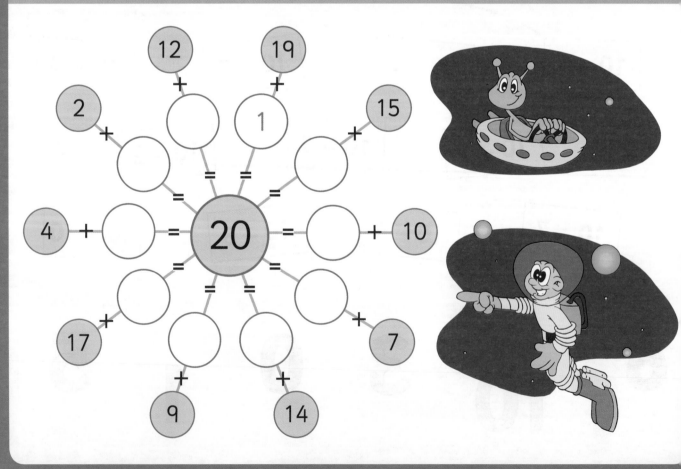

Learn the numbers that subtract from 20.

20 − 0 = 20	20 − 7 = 13	20 − 14 = 6
20 − 1 = 19	20 − 8 = 12	20 − 15 = 5
20 − 2 = 18	20 − 9 = 11	20 − 16 = 4
20 − 3 = 17	20 − 10 = 10	20 − 17 = 3
20 − 4 = 16	20 − 11 = 9	20 − 18 = 2
20 − 5 = 15	20 − 12 = 8	20 − 19 = 1
20 − 6 = 14	20 − 13 = 7	20 − 20 = 0

Complete the calculations by filling in the boxes.

20 − 8 = 12   20 − ☐ = 17

20 − ☐ = 1   20 − ☐ = 0

20 − 13 = ☐   20 − 9 = ☐

20 − 7 = ☐   20 − 15 = ☐

20 − ☐ = 10   20 − ☐ = 14

20 − 5 = ☐   20 − 2 = ☐

Adding & Subtracting by Counting

You can add by counting on in ones or tens.
Here's an example.

$2 + 3 = 5$

$$2 \xrightarrow{+1} 3 \xrightarrow{+1} 4 \xrightarrow{+1} 5$$

You can subtract by counting back in ones or tens.
Here's an example.

$95 - 30 = 65$

$$95 \xrightarrow{-10} 85 \xrightarrow{-10} 75 \xrightarrow{-10} 65$$

Draw lines to match each calculation to the ball with the correct answer.

$19 - 9 =$

$12 + 2 =$

$17 - 6 =$

$25 - 20 =$

$3 + 10 =$

10 4 13 1 12 3 5 14 7 8 11

Draw the stick man on the correct step using the instructions on the signposts.

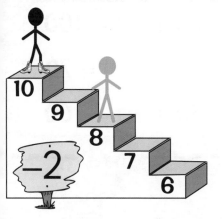 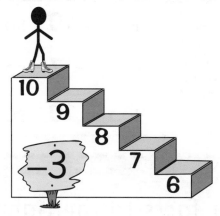 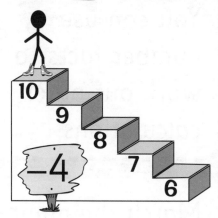

 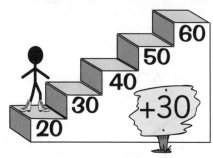 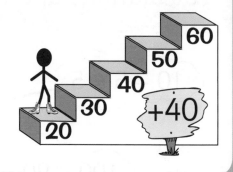

Write the missing numbers in the boxes.

4 (+10) = 14   9 (+10) = ☐   15 (−10) = ☐

11 (−10) = ☐   12 (+20) = ☐   24 (+40) = ☐

17 (+70) = ☐   58 (−30) = ☐   82 (−40) = ☐

34 (−20) = ☐   99 (−90) = ☐   76 (+20) = ☐

13

Using Number Facts

You can use number facts to work out other calculations.

$2 + 8 = \mathbf{10}$ so $20 + 80 = \mathbf{100}$

$10 - 3 = \mathbf{7}$ so $100 - 30 = \mathbf{70}$

$5 + 5 = \mathbf{10}$ so $50 + 50 = \mathbf{100}$

Match the number facts to the right calculations and use them to fill in the boxes.

$10 - 5 = 5$

$40 + 60 = \boxed{}$

$7 + 3 = 10$

$100 - 90 = \boxed{}$

$100 - 50 = \boxed{50}$

$10 - 9 = 1$

$70 + 30 = \boxed{}$

$4 + 6 = 10$

Use number facts to fill in the missing numbers.

$100 - 30 = \boxed{}$

$\boxed{} = 70 + 30$

$90 + \boxed{} = 100$

$40 + \boxed{} = 100$

$100 - 50 = \boxed{}$

$100 - 80 = \boxed{}$

$\boxed{} = 100 - 10$

$100 - \boxed{} = 20$

$\boxed{} + 60 = 100$

Checking with Inverses

Inverse means opposite. Addition and subtraction are inverses.

$4 + 5 = 9$ → $9 - 5 = 4$
→ $9 - 4 = 5$

You can use inverses to check answers. ▷

Lou says, "$15 - 7 = 8$."
Is Lou right?
$7 + 8 = 15$. So Lou **is** right.

Fill in the boxes to complete the inverses.

$14 - 6 = 8$	$8 + 40 = 48$	$60 - 9 = 51$
$8 + 6 = \boxed{}$	$48 - \boxed{} = 40$	$60 - 51 = \boxed{9}$
$14 - 8 = \boxed{6}$	$\boxed{} - 40 = \boxed{}$	$\boxed{} + 9 = \boxed{}$

Decide which of these are correct by working out the inverse. Put a tick or cross in each box.

$23 - 8 = 14$ $8 + 14 = 22$	$23 - 5 = 13$	☐
$17 - 4 = 13$ ☐	$8 + 90 = 98$	☐
$25 + 20 = 45$ ☐	$10 + 17 = 37$	☐

15

Bigger Numbers

It's easier to add bigger numbers if you split them up. Here's an example. ⟹ **30 + 23**

Split up the smaller number into **tens** and **ones**. ⟹ 23 ⟨ 20 **2 tens** / 3 **3 ones**

Count on in **tens** from the big number. ⟹ 30 + 20 = **50**

Count on in **ones** to get the **answer**. ⟹ 50 + 3 = **53**

Fill in the boxes to find the answers.

60 + 23 23 ⟨ 20 / 3

60 + 20 = 80

80 + 3 = ☐

51 + 16 16 ⟨ 10 / 6

51 + 10 = ☐

☐ + ☐ = ☐

77 + 22 22 ⟨ ☐ / ☐

☐ + ☐ = ☐

☐ + ☐ = ☐

46 + 43 ☐ / ☐

☐ + ☐ = ☐

☐ + ☐ = ☐

57 + 14 ☐ / ☐

☐ + ☐ = ☐

☐ + ☐ = ☐

45 + 36 ☐ / ☐

☐ + ☐ = ☐

☐ + ☐ = ☐

Practise & Learn

Mental Maths
Ages 5-7
Answers

This section shows each of the pages from the book with the answers filled in.

The pages are laid out in the same way as the book itself, so the questions can be easily marked by you, or by your child.

There are also helpful learning tips with some of the pages.

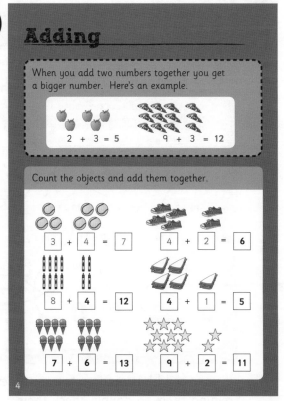

4

Adding

When you add two numbers together you get a bigger number. Here's an example.

2 + 3 = 5   9 + 3 = 12

Count the objects and add them together.

3 + 4 = 7   4 + 2 = 6

8 + 4 = 12   4 + 1 = 5

7 + 6 = 13   9 + 2 = 11

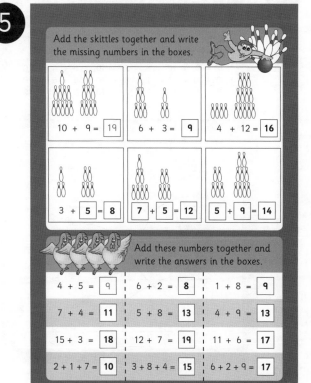

5

Add the skittles together and write the missing numbers in the boxes.

10 + 9 = 19   6 + 3 = 9   4 + 12 = 16

3 + 5 = 8   7 + 5 = 12   5 + 9 = 14

Add these numbers together and write the answers in the boxes.

4 + 5 = 9	6 + 2 = 8	1 + 8 = 9
7 + 4 = 11	5 + 8 = 13	4 + 9 = 13
15 + 3 = 18	12 + 7 = 19	11 + 6 = 17
2 + 1 + 7 = 10	3 + 8 + 4 = 15	6 + 2 + 9 = 17

Remind your child that addition can be done in any order. It may help them to put the larger number first.

⑥ Subtracting

When you subtract, you take away one number from another to get a smaller number. Here's an example.

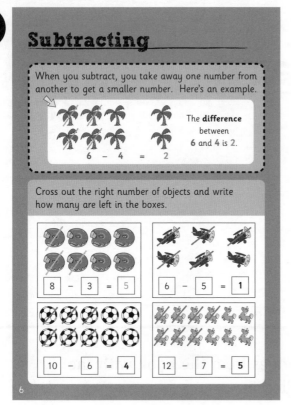

The **difference** between **6** and **4** is **2**.

6 − 4 = 2

Cross out the right number of objects and write how many are left in the boxes.

8 − 3 = 5

6 − 5 = 1

10 − 6 = 4

12 − 7 = 5

6

⑦

Work out the answers to the questions and write your answers in the boxes.

9 − 7 = 2   10 − 4 = 6

19 − 15 = 4   12 − 1 = 11

8 − 5 = 3   16 − 8 = 8

What is 14 take away 4?   10

What is the difference between six and thirteen?   7

What is 3 less than 11?   8

Fill in the boxes to complete the calculations below.

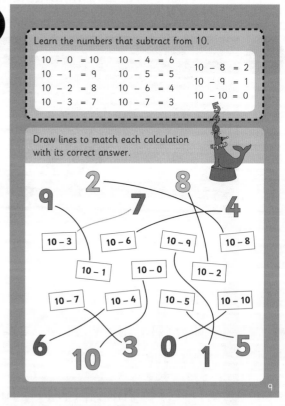

	9			15	−	4	=	11
	−			−		−		−
14	−	2	= 12	6		3		3
	=			=		=		=
	7		10		−	9	=	1	8
			−					
			2	−	1	=	1	

7

Remind your child that subtraction, unlike addition, can't be done in any order. The largest number must come first.

⑧ Number Facts to 10

Learn the pairs of numbers that add up to 10. Numbers can be added together in any order.

10 + 0 = 10   8 + 2 = 10   6 + 4 = 10
0 + 10 = 10   2 + 8 = 10   4 + 6 = 10
9 + 1 = 10   7 + 3 = 10   5 + 5 = 10
1 + 9 = 10   3 + 7 = 10

Draw lines so that each pair of boats adds up to 10.

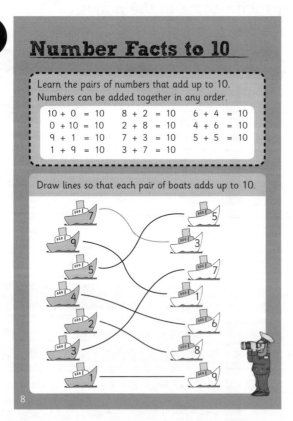

8

⑨

Learn the numbers that subtract from 10.

10 − 0 = 10   10 − 4 = 6   10 − 8 = 2
10 − 1 = 9   10 − 5 = 5   10 − 9 = 1
10 − 2 = 8   10 − 6 = 4   10 − 10 = 0
10 − 3 = 7   10 − 7 = 3

Draw lines to match each calculation with its correct answer.

2   8

9   7   4

10 − 3   10 − 6   10 − 9   10 − 8

10 − 1   10 − 0   10 − 2

10 − 7   10 − 4   10 − 5   10 − 10

6   3   5
10   0   1

9

If your child has made a few mistakes, remind them to double check their work next time — it's a really good habit for them to get into.

Number Facts to 20

Learn the pairs of numbers that add up to 20.

20 + 0 = 20	3 + 17 = 20	13 + 7 = 20
0 + 20 = 20	16 + 4 = 20	7 + 13 = 20
19 + 1 = 20	4 + 16 = 20	12 + 8 = 20
1 + 19 = 20	15 + 5 = 20	8 + 12 = 20
18 + 2 = 20	5 + 15 = 20	11 + 9 = 20
2 + 18 = 20	14 + 6 = 20	9 + 11 = 20
17 + 3 = 20	6 + 14 = 20	10 + 10 = 20

Make all the lines on the star add up to 20.

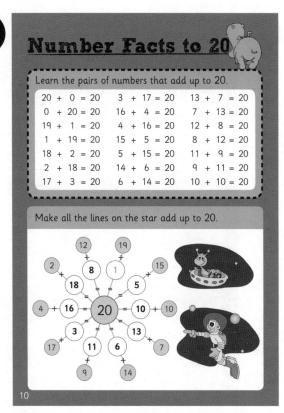

Ensure that your child is confident at answering questions on number facts, then encourage them to build up speed.

Learn the numbers that subtract from 20.

20 − 0 = 20	20 − 7 = 13	20 − 14 = 6
20 − 1 = 19	20 − 8 = 12	20 − 15 = 5
20 − 2 = 18	20 − 9 = 11	20 − 16 = 4
20 − 3 = 17	20 − 10 = 10	20 − 17 = 3
20 − 4 = 16	20 − 11 = 9	20 − 18 = 2
20 − 5 = 15	20 − 12 = 8	20 − 19 = 1
20 − 6 = 14	20 − 13 = 7	20 − 20 = 0

Complete the calculations by filling in the boxes.

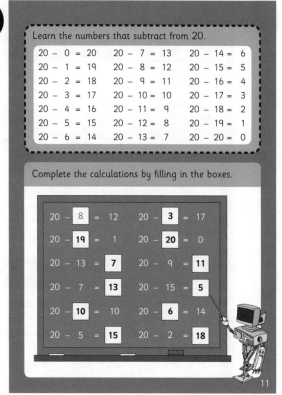

20 − **8** = 12		20 − **3** = 17
20 − **19** = 1		20 − **20** = 0
20 − 13 = **7**		20 − 9 = **11**
20 − 7 = **13**		20 − 15 = **5**
20 − **10** = 10		20 − **6** = 14
20 − 5 = **15**		20 − 2 = **18**

Adding & Subtracting by Counting

You can add by counting on in ones or tens. Here's an example.

2 + 3 = 5

You can subtract by counting back in ones or tens. Here's an example.

95 − 30 = 65

Draw lines to match each calculation to the ball with the correct answer.

19 − 9 =
12 + 2 =
17 − 6 =
25 − 20 =
3 + 10 =

Draw the stick man on the correct step using the instructions on the signposts.

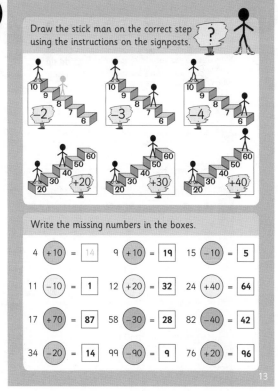

Write the missing numbers in the boxes.

4 (+10) = 14	9 (+10) = **19**	15 (−10) = **5**
11 (−10) = **1**	12 (+20) = **32**	24 (+40) = **64**
17 (+70) = **87**	58 (−30) = **28**	82 (−40) = **42**
34 (−20) = **14**	99 (−90) = **9**	76 (+20) = **96**

If your child is having difficulty with the questions in the second exercise, drawing a number line on a separate piece of paper will help them to count on and back in tens.

Using Number Facts

You can use number facts to work out other calculations.

$2 + 8 = 10$ so $20 + 80 = 100$
$10 - 3 = 7$ so $100 - 30 = 70$
$5 + 5 = 10$ so $50 + 50 = 100$

Match the number facts to the right calculations and use them to fill in the boxes.

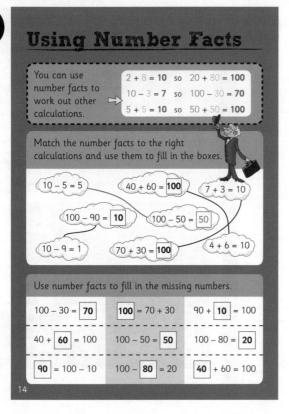

$10 - 5 = 5$

$40 + 60 = 100$

$7 + 3 = 10$

$100 - 90 = 10$

$100 - 50 = 50$

$10 - 9 = 1$

$70 + 30 = 100$

$4 + 6 = 10$

Use number facts to fill in the missing numbers.

$100 - 30 = 70$	$100 = 70 + 30$	$90 + 10 = 100$
$40 + 60 = 100$	$100 - 50 = 50$	$100 - 80 = 20$
$90 = 100 - 10$	$100 - 80 = 20$	$40 + 60 = 100$

Checking with Inverses

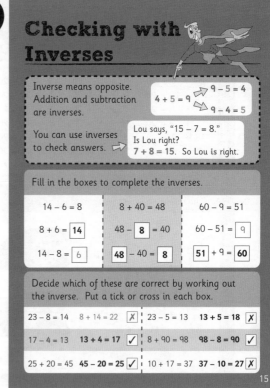

Inverse means opposite. Addition and subtraction are inverses.

$4 + 5 = 9$

$9 - 5 = 4$
$9 - 4 = 5$

You can use inverses to check answers.

Lou says, "15 – 7 = 8." Is Lou right?
$7 + 8 = 15$. So Lou is right.

Fill in the boxes to complete the inverses.

$14 - 6 = 8$	$8 + 40 = 48$	$60 - 9 = 51$
$8 + 6 = 14$	$48 - 8 = 40$	$60 - 51 = 9$
$14 - 8 = 6$	$48 - 40 = 8$	$51 + 9 = 60$

Decide which of these are correct by working out the inverse. Put a tick or cross in each box.

$23 - 8 = 14$ $8 + 14 = 22$ ✗	$23 - 5 = 13$ $13 + 5 = 18$ ✗	
$17 - 4 = 13$ $13 + 4 = 17$ ✓	$8 + 90 = 98$ $98 - 8 = 90$ ✓	
$25 + 20 = 45$ $45 - 20 = 25$ ✓	$10 + 17 = 37$ $37 - 10 = 27$ ✗	

There are other inverse calculations that your child could use here.

Bigger Numbers

It's easier to add bigger numbers if you split them up. Here's an example.

$30 + 23$

Split up the smaller number into **tens** and **ones**.

23
20 **2 tens**
3 **3 ones**

Count on in **tens** from the big number. $30 + 20 = 50$

Count on in **ones** to get the **answer**. $50 + 3 = 53$

Fill in the boxes to find the answers.

60 + 23
23 20 3
$60 + 20 = 80$
$80 + 3 = 83$

51 + 16
16 10 6
$51 + 10 = 61$
$61 + 6 = 67$

77 + 22
22 20 2
$77 + 20 = 97$
$97 + 2 = 99$

46 + 43
43 40 3
$46 + 40 = 86$
$86 + 3 = 89$

57 + 14
14 10 4
$57 + 10 = 67$
$67 + 4 = 71$

45 + 36
36 30 6
$45 + 30 = 75$
$75 + 6 = 81$

If your child is struggling with splitting numbers, help them to identify the tens and ones in each number.

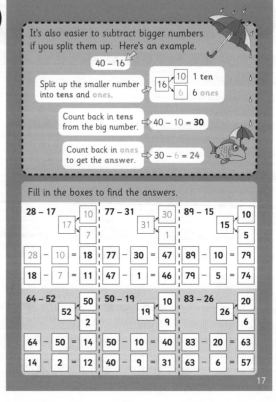

It's also easier to subtract bigger numbers if you split them up. Here's an example.

$40 - 16$

Split up the smaller number into **tens** and **ones**.

16 10 **1 ten** 6 **6 ones**

Count back in **tens** from the big number. $40 - 10 = 30$

Count back in **ones** to get the **answer**. $30 - 6 = 24$

Fill in the boxes to find the answers.

28 – 17
17 10 7
$28 - 10 = 18$
$18 - 7 = 11$

77 – 31
31 30 1
$77 - 30 = 47$
$47 - 1 = 46$

89 – 15
15 10 5
$89 - 10 = 79$
$79 - 5 = 74$

64 – 52
52 50 2
$64 - 50 = 14$
$14 - 2 = 12$

50 – 19
19 10 9
$50 - 10 = 40$
$40 - 9 = 31$

83 – 26
26 20 6
$83 - 20 = 63$
$63 - 6 = 57$

Multiplying by 2

When you multiply by 2, it's the same as adding up groups of two. Here's an example.

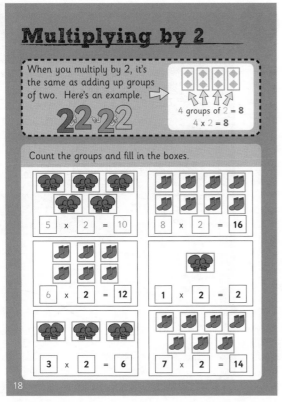

4 groups of 2 = **8**
4 x 2 = **8**

Count the groups and fill in the boxes.

5	x	2	=	10
8	x	2	=	**16**
6	x	2	=	12
1	x	2	=	2
3	x	2	=	6
7	x	2	=	14

If your child is struggling with multiplying by 2, it may help to get them to practise counting in twos out loud.

Dividing by 2

When you divide by 2, you see how many groups of two there are. Here's an example.

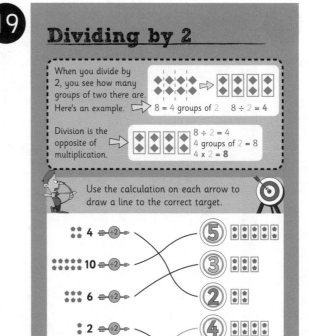

8 = 4 groups of 2   8 ÷ 2 = **4**

Division is the opposite of multiplication.

8 ÷ 2 = 4
4 groups of 2 = 8
4 x 2 = **8**

Use the calculation on each arrow to draw a line to the correct target.

4 ÷2
10 ÷2
6 ÷2
2 ÷2
8 ÷2

(5) (3) (2) (4) (1)

Multiplying by 5

When you multiply by 5, it's the same as adding up groups of five. Here's an example.

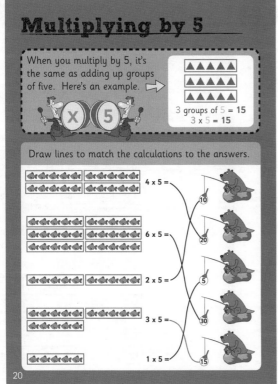

3 groups of 5 = **15**
3 x 5 = **15**

Draw lines to match the calculations to the answers.

4 x 5 =
6 x 5 =
2 x 5 =
3 x 5 =
1 x 5 =

10
20
5
30
15

Dividing by 5

When you divide by 5, you see how many groups of five there are. Here's an example.

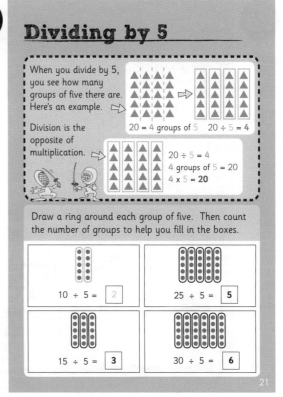

20 = 4 groups of 5   20 ÷ 5 = 4

Division is the opposite of multiplication.

20 ÷ 5 = 4
4 groups of 5 = 20
4 x 5 = **20**

Draw a ring around each group of five. Then count the number of groups to help you fill in the boxes.

10 ÷ 5 = 2

25 ÷ 5 = **5**

15 ÷ 5 = **3**

30 ÷ 5 = **6**

Make sure your child understands that division is the opposite of multiplication. They can use the multiplications they know to work out the answers to divisions.

Multiplying by 10

When you multiply by 10, it's the same as adding up groups of ten. Here's an example.

3 groups of 10 = 30
3 x 10 = **30**

Count the groups and fill in the boxes.

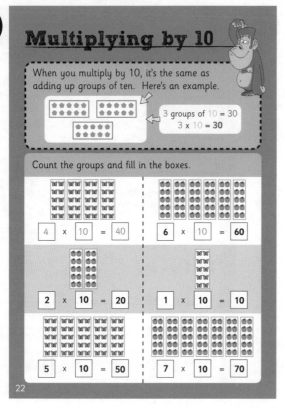

4 x 10 = 40

6 x 10 = 60

2 x 10 = 20

1 x 10 = 10

5 x 10 = 50

7 x 10 = 70

Dividing by 10

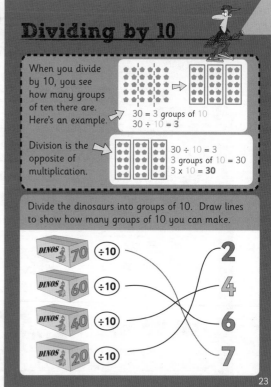

When you divide by 10, you see how many groups of ten there are. Here's an example.

30 = 3 groups of 10
30 ÷ 10 = **3**

Division is the opposite of multiplication.

30 ÷ 10 = 3
3 groups of 10 = 30
3 x 10 = **30**

Divide the dinosaurs into groups of 10. Draw lines to show how many groups of 10 you can make.

DINOS 70 ÷10
DINOS 60 ÷10
DINOS 40 ÷10
DINOS 20 ÷10

2
4
6
7

If your child is struggling with multiplying and dividing by 10, encourage them to practise counting on and back in tens.

Two Times Table

Here is the two times table.

Use the sets of dots to help you count to each number in the two times table.

1 x 2 = 2	:
2 x 2 = 4	::
3 x 2 = 6	:::
4 x 2 = 8	::::
5 x 2 = 10	:::::
6 x 2 = 12	::::::
7 x 2 = 14	:::::::
8 x 2 = 16	::::::::
9 x 2 = 18	:::::::::
10 x 2 = 20	::::::::::
11 x 2 = 22	:::::::::::
12 x 2 = 24	::::::::::::

Complete the calculations by filling in the boxes.

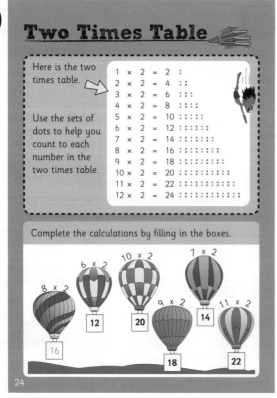

8 x 2 — 16
6 x 2 — 12
10 x 2 — 20
9 x 2 — 18
1 x 2 — 14
11 x 2 — 22

Division is the opposite of multiplication. If you know your times tables, you can work out some divisions. Here's an example.

6 ÷ 2 = ?
Using the 2 times table, you know that 3 x 2 = 6
This means that 6 ÷ 2 = 3

Fill in the boxes to complete the calculations.

2 →(x2) 4 →(x2) 8 →(x2) 16

20 →(÷2) 10 →(÷2) 5 →(x2) 10

6 →(÷2) 3 →(x2) 6 →(x2) 12

Fill in the boxes to complete the calculations.

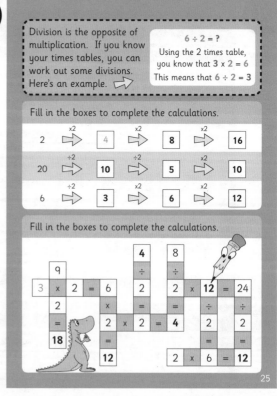

4   8
9
3 x 2 = 6   2   2 x 12 = 24
2   x   ÷   ÷
=   =   =
18   2 x 2 = 4   2   2
=   =
12   2 x 6 = 12

If your child finds these questions tricky, help them learn their 2 times table. This will make multiplying and dividing by two much quicker.

Five Times Table

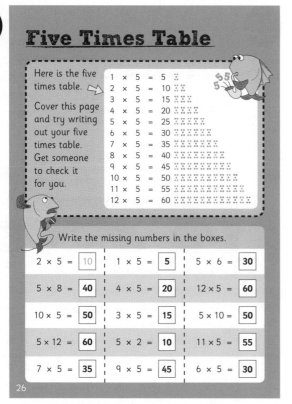

Here is the five times table. Cover this page and try writing out your five times table. Get someone to check it for you.

1	×	5	=	5
2	×	5	=	10
3	×	5	=	15
4	×	5	=	20
5	×	5	=	25
6	×	5	=	30
7	×	5	=	35
8	×	5	=	40
9	×	5	=	45
10	×	5	=	50
11	×	5	=	55
12	×	5	=	60

Write the missing numbers in the boxes.

2 × 5 = 10   1 × 5 = 5   5 × 6 = 30

5 × 8 = 40   4 × 5 = 20   12 × 5 = 60

10 × 5 = 50   3 × 5 = 15   5 × 10 = 50

5 × 12 = 60   5 × 2 = 10   11 × 5 = 55

7 × 5 = 35   9 × 5 = 45   6 × 5 = 30

26

Make sure your child understands that multiplication can be done in any order — 6 × 5 is the same as 5 × 6.

Division is the opposite of multiplication. If you know your times tables, you can work out some divisions. Here's an example.

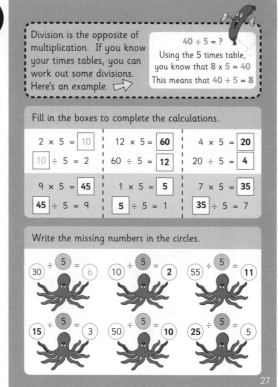

40 ÷ 5 = ?
Using the 5 times table, you know that 8 x 5 = 40
This means that 40 ÷ 5 = 8

Fill in the boxes to complete the calculations.

2 × 5 = 10   12 × 5 = 60   4 × 5 = 20
10 ÷ 5 = 2   60 ÷ 5 = 12   20 ÷ 5 = 4

9 × 5 = 45   1 × 5 = 5   7 × 5 = 35
45 ÷ 5 = 9   5 ÷ 5 = 1   35 ÷ 5 = 7

Write the missing numbers in the circles.

30 ÷ 5 = 6   10 ÷ 5 = 2   55 ÷ 5 = 11

15 ÷ 5 = 3   50 ÷ 5 = 10   25 ÷ 5 = 5

27

Ten Times Table

Here is the ten times table.

The ten times table is the same as counting in tens.

+10 +10 +10
10 20 30 40

1	×	10	=	10
2	×	10	=	20
3	×	10	=	30
4	×	10	=	40
5	×	10	=	50
6	×	10	=	60
7	×	10	=	70
8	×	10	=	80
9	×	10	=	90
10	×	10	=	100
11	×	10	=	110
12	×	10	=	120

Multiply each number by ten to fill in the boxes.

x10

= 30
= 50
= 90
= 70
= 60

28

Make sure your child knows their 5 and 10 times tables. If not, encourage them to practise until they are confident with them both.

Division is the opposite of multiplication. If you know your times tables, you can work out some divisions. Here's an example.

90 ÷ 10 = ?
Using the 10 times table, you know that 9 x 10 = 90
This means that
90 ÷ 10 = 9

Colour in the correct answers to the calculations to make a path for the seal.

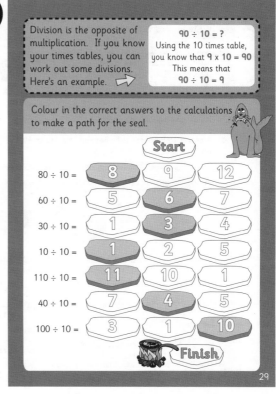

Start

80 ÷ 10 =   8   9   12
60 ÷ 10 =   5   6   7
30 ÷ 10 =   1   3   4
10 ÷ 10 =   1   2   5
110 ÷ 10 =   11   10   1
40 ÷ 10 =   7   4   5
100 ÷ 10 =   3   1   10

Finish

29

Problem Solving

Some questions won't tell you whether you need to add, subtract, multiply or divide. You have to work out what to do. Here's an example.

Clare has **20** letters. She delivers **6** letters. How many letters does she have left?

You need to find the difference between **20** and **6**. Subtract **6** from **20**.

20 – 6 = 14 letters

The poster shows the prices at a cinema. Draw lines to match the groups to the correct prices.

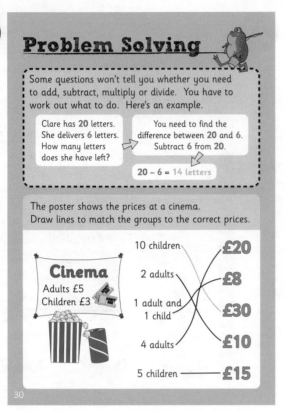

Cinema
Adults £5
Children £3

10 children
2 adults
1 adult and 1 child
4 adults
5 children

£20
£8
£30
£10
£15

Write the answers to these questions in the boxes.

Kaye has 18 cakes. She eats 8 cakes. How many cakes does she have left? `10`

Rachael has 20 cakes. She shares them between 5 friends. How many cakes does each friend get? `4`

Andre has 2 orange cakes, 5 banana cakes and 4 chocolate cakes. How many cakes does he have altogether? `11`

Write the answers to these questions in the boxes.

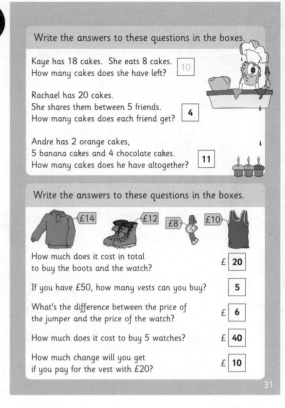

£14   £12   £8   £10

How much does it cost in total to buy the boots and the watch? £ `20`

If you have £50, how many vests can you buy? `5`

What's the difference between the price of the jumper and the price of the watch? £ `6`

How much does it cost to buy 5 watches? £ `40`

How much change will you get if you pay for the vest with £20? £ `10`

Your child might struggle to work out whether they need to add, subtract, multiply or divide. You can help them by working through some examples together.

Write the answers to these questions in the boxes.

Adil has 5 pizzas. Each pizza is cut into 6 slices. How many slices of pizza are there altogether? `30`

18 people are at a party. 11 of them drink lemonade and the rest drink apple juice. How many people drink apple juice? `7`

Alex has 16 balloons. Leila has half as many as Alex. How many balloons does Leila have? `8`

Write the answers to these questions in the boxes.

25p   8p   53p   10p

How much does it cost to buy 2 mushrooms? `16` p

Roger has 90p. How many tomatoes can he buy? `9`

Laura has 20p. She buys 1 mushroom. How much change does she get? `12` p

How much does it cost to buy 1 cabbage and 1 carrot? `78` p

If your child finds word problems difficult, let them write down the calculation they need to do. Then they can work out the answer in their head.

Race to the Beehive

You'll need a counter for each player and a dice. Place your counters at the start, and take it in turns to roll the dice once. Follow the instructions when you land on them.

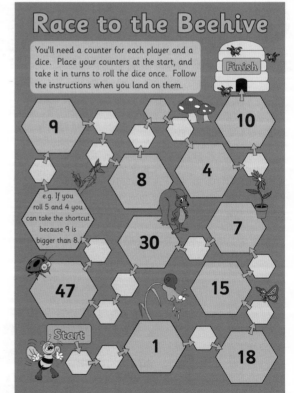

Finish

9   10

8   4

e.g. If you roll 5 and 4 you can take the shortcut because 9 is bigger than 8.

30   7

47   15

Start   1   18

It's also easier to subtract bigger numbers if you split them up. Here's an example.

40 – 16

Split up the smaller number into **tens** and **ones**.

16 → 10 **1 ten**
→ 6 **6 ones**

Count back in **tens** from the big number.
⇒ 40 – 10 = **30**

Count back in **ones** to get the **answer**.
⇒ 30 – 6 = **24**

Fill in the boxes to find the answers.

28 – 17

17 → 10
→ 7

28 – 10 = ☐
☐ – 7 = ☐

77 – 31

31 → 30
→ 1

☐ – ☐ = ☐
☐ – ☐ = ☐

89 – 15

☐ → ☐
→ ☐

☐ – ☐ = ☐
☐ – ☐ = ☐

64 – 52

☐ → ☐
→ ☐

☐ – ☐ = ☐
☐ – ☐ = ☐

50 – 19

☐ → ☐
→ ☐

☐ – ☐ = ☐
☐ – ☐ = ☐

83 – 26

☐ → ☐
→ ☐

☐ – ☐ = ☐
☐ – ☐ = ☐

Multiplying by 2

When you multiply by 2, it's the same as adding up groups of two. Here's an example.

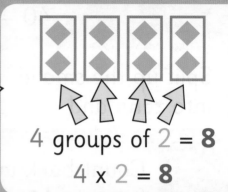

4 groups of 2 = **8**

4 x 2 = **8**

Count the groups and fill in the boxes.

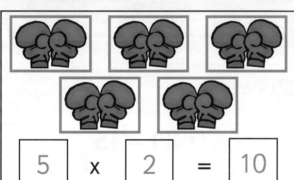

| 5 | x | 2 | = | 10 |

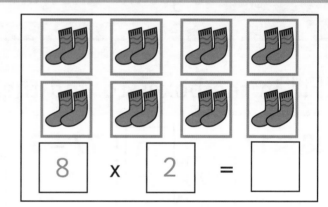

| 8 | x | 2 | = | |

| 6 | x | | = | |

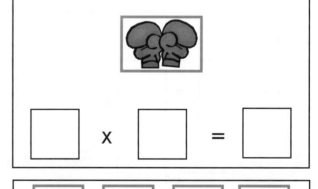

| | x | | = | |

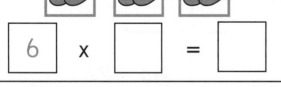

| | x | | = | |

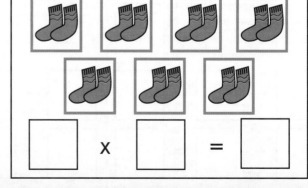

| | x | | = | |

Dividing by 2

When you divide by 2, you see how many groups of two there are. Here's an example.

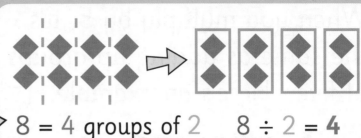

8 = 4 groups of 2   8 ÷ 2 = **4**

Division is the opposite of multiplication.

8 ÷ 2 = 4
4 groups of 2 = 8
4 x 2 = **8**

 Use the calculation on each arrow to draw a line to the correct target.

 4

 ⑤

10

 ③

 6

②

 2

④

8

 ①

Multiplying by 5

When you multiply by 5, it's the same as adding up groups of five. Here's an example.

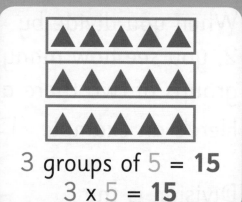

3 groups of 5 = **15**

3 x 5 = **15**

Draw lines to match the calculations to the answers.

 4 x 5 =

 10

 6 x 5 =

 20

2 x 5 =

 5

3 x 5 =

 30

1 x 5 =

 15

20

Dividing by 5

When you divide by 5, you see how many groups of five there are. Here's an example.

Division is the opposite of multiplication.

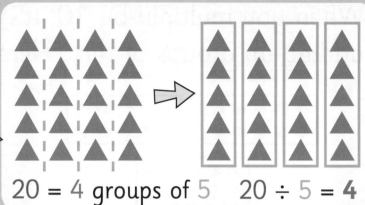

20 = 4 groups of 5   20 ÷ 5 = **4**

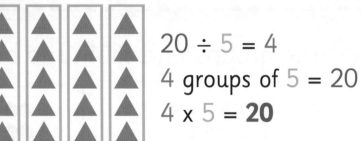

$20 \div 5 = 4$

4 groups of 5 = 20

$4 \times 5 = \textbf{20}$

Draw a ring around each group of five. Then count the number of groups to help you fill in the boxes.

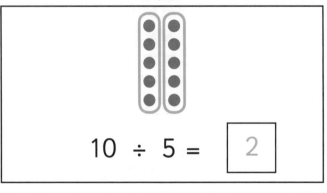

10 ÷ 5 = 2

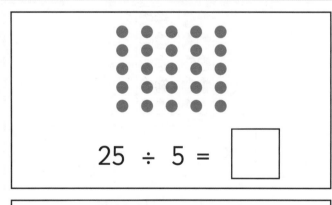

25 ÷ 5 =

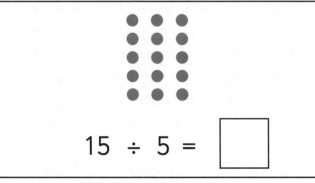

15 ÷ 5 =

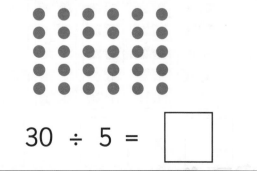

30 ÷ 5 =

21

Multiplying by 10

When you multiply by 10, it's the same as adding up groups of ten. Here's an example.

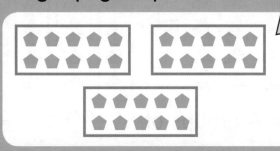

3 groups of 10 = 30
3 x 10 = **30**

Count the groups and fill in the boxes.

4 x 10 = 40

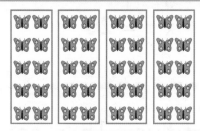

☐ x 10 = ☐

☐ x ☐ = ☐

☐ x ☐ = ☐

☐ x ☐ = ☐

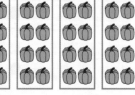

☐ x ☐ = ☐

Dividing by 10

When you divide by 10, you see how many groups of ten there are. Here's an example.

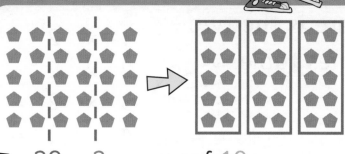

30 = 3 groups of 10
30 ÷ 10 = **3**

Division is the opposite of multiplication.

30 ÷ 10 = 3
3 groups of 10 = 30
3 x 10 = **30**

Divide the dinosaurs into groups of 10. Draw lines to show how many groups of 10 you can make.

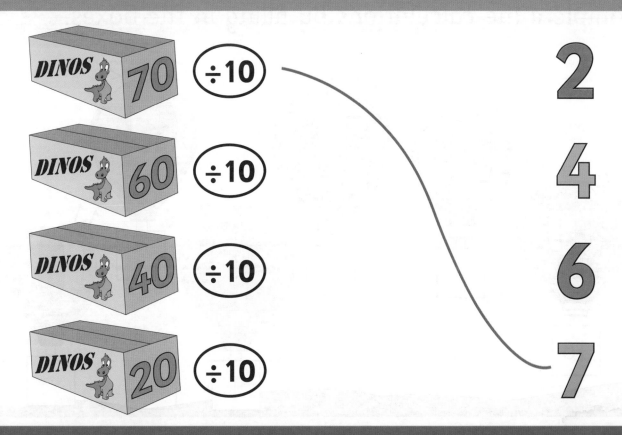

DINOS 70 ÷10

DINOS 60 ÷10

DINOS 40 ÷10

DINOS 20 ÷10

2

4

6

7

Two Times Table

Here is the two times table.

Use the sets of dots to help you count to each number in the two times table.

1	×	2	=	2	
2	×	2	=	4	
3	×	2	=	6	
4	×	2	=	8	
5	×	2	=	10	
6	×	2	=	12	
7	×	2	=	14	
8	×	2	=	16	
9	×	2	=	18	
10	×	2	=	20	
11	×	2	=	22	
12	×	2	=	24	

Complete the calculations by filling in the boxes.

8 x 2

16

6 x 2

10 x 2

9 x 2

7 x 2

11 x 2

Division is the opposite of multiplication. If you know your times tables, you can work out some divisions. Here's an example.

$6 \div 2 = ?$

Using the 2 times table, you know that $3 \times 2 = 6$
This means that $6 \div 2 = 3$

Fill in the boxes to complete the calculations.

2 —x2→ 4 —x2→ ☐ —x2→ ☐

20 —÷2→ ☐ —÷2→ ☐ —x2→ ☐

6 —÷2→ ☐ —x2→ ☐ —x2→ ☐

Fill in the boxes to complete the calculations.

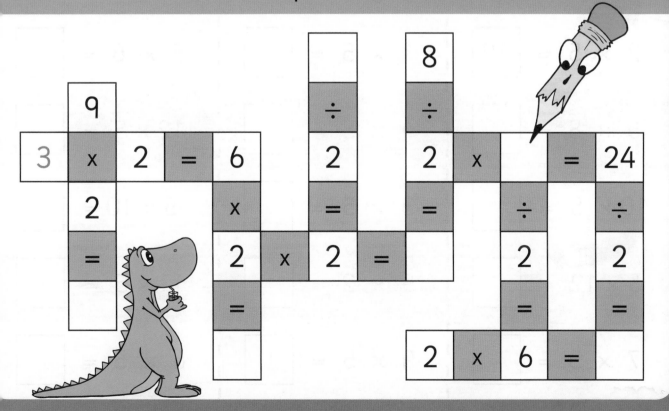

Five Times Table

Here is the five times table.

Cover this page and try writing out your five times table. Get someone to check it for you.

1	× 5	=	5	
2	× 5	=	10	
3	× 5	=	15	
4	× 5	=	20	
5	× 5	=	25	
6	× 5	=	30	
7	× 5	=	35	
8	× 5	=	40	
9	× 5	=	45	
10	× 5	=	50	
11	× 5	=	55	
12	× 5	=	60	

Write the missing numbers in the boxes.

2 × 5 = 10

5 × 8 = ☐

10 × 5 = ☐

5 × 12 = ☐

7 × 5 = ☐

1 × 5 = ☐

4 × 5 = ☐

3 × 5 = ☐

5 × 2 = ☐

9 × 5 = ☐

5 × 6 = ☐

12 × 5 = ☐

5 × 10 = ☐

11 × 5 = ☐

6 × 5 = ☐

Division is the opposite of multiplication. If you know your times tables, you can work out some divisions. Here's an example. ➡

$40 \div 5 = ?$

Using the 5 times table, you know that $8 \times 5 = 40$

This means that $40 \div 5 = 8$

Fill in the boxes to complete the calculations.

$2 \times 5 = \boxed{10}$

$\boxed{10} \div 5 = 2$

$12 \times 5 = \boxed{}$

$60 \div 5 = \boxed{}$

$4 \times 5 = \boxed{}$

$20 \div 5 = \boxed{}$

$9 \times 5 = \boxed{}$

$\boxed{} \div 5 = 9$

$1 \times 5 = \boxed{}$

$\boxed{} \div 5 = 1$

$7 \times 5 = \boxed{}$

$\boxed{} \div 5 = 7$

Write the missing numbers in the circles.

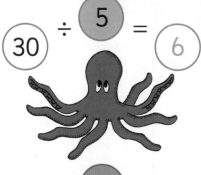

$30 \div 5 = 6$

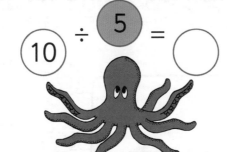

$10 \div 5 = \bigcirc$

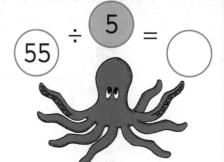

$55 \div 5 = \bigcirc$

$\bigcirc \div 5 = 3$

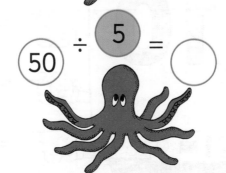

$50 \div 5 = \bigcirc$

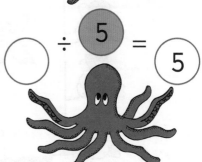

$\bigcirc \div 5 = 5$

Ten Times Table

Here is the ten times table.

The ten times table is the same as counting in tens.

10 $\xrightarrow{+10}$ 20 $\xrightarrow{+10}$ 30 $\xrightarrow{+10}$ 40

1	×	10	=	10
2	×	10	=	20
3	×	10	=	30
4	×	10	=	40
5	×	10	=	50
6	×	10	=	60
7	×	10	=	70
8	×	10	=	80
9	×	10	=	90
10	×	10	=	100
11	×	10	=	110
12	×	10	=	120

Multiply each number by ten to fill in the boxes.

3, 5, 9, 7, 6 ×10 = 30, =, =, =, =

28

Division is the opposite of multiplication. If you know your times tables, you can work out some divisions. Here's an example. ▷

90 ÷ 10 = ?
Using the 10 times table, you know that 9 x 10 = 90
This means that
90 ÷ 10 = 9

Colour in the correct answers to the calculations to make a path for the seal.

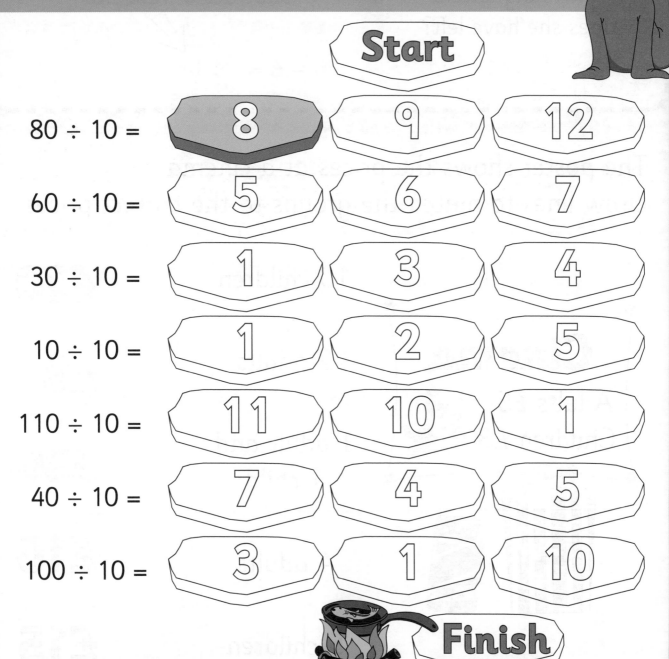

Start

80 ÷ 10 =	8	9	12
60 ÷ 10 =	5	6	7
30 ÷ 10 =	1	3	4
10 ÷ 10 =	1	2	5
110 ÷ 10 =	11	10	1
40 ÷ 10 =	7	4	5
100 ÷ 10 =	3	1	10

Finish

29

Problem Solving

Some questions won't tell you whether you need to add, subtract, multiply or divide. You have to work out what to do. Here's an example.

> Clare has **20** letters. She delivers **6** letters. How many letters does she have left?

> You need to find the difference between **20** and **6**. Subtract **6** from **20**.

> 20 – 6 = **14 letters**

The poster shows the prices at a cinema.
Draw lines to match the groups to the correct prices.

10 children	**£20**
2 adults	**£8**
1 adult and 1 child	**£30**
4 adults	**£10**
5 children	**£15**

Cinema
Adults £5
Children £3

Write the answers to these questions in the boxes.

Kaye has 18 cakes. She eats 8 cakes.
How many cakes does she have left? 10

Rachael has 20 cakes.
She shares them between 5 friends.
How many cakes does each friend get? ☐

Andre has 2 orange cakes,
5 banana cakes and 4 chocolate cakes.
How many cakes does he have altogether? ☐

Write the answers to these questions in the boxes.

£14   £12   £8   £10

How much does it cost in total
to buy the boots and the watch? £ ☐

If you have £50, how many vests can you buy? ☐

What's the difference between the price of
the jumper and the price of the watch? £ ☐

How much does it cost to buy 5 watches? £ ☐

How much change will you get
if you pay for the vest with £20? £ ☐

Write the answers to these questions in the boxes.

Adil has 5 pizzas. Each pizza is cut into 6 slices. How many slices of pizza are there altogether? ☐

18 people are at a party. 11 of them drink lemonade and the rest drink apple juice. How many people drink apple juice? ☐

Alex has 16 balloons. Leila has half as many as Alex. How many balloons does Leila have? ☐

Write the answers to these questions in the boxes.

25p   8p   53p   10p

How much does it cost to buy 2 mushrooms? ☐ p

Roger has 90p. How many tomatoes can he buy? ☐

Laura has 20p. She buys 1 mushroom. How much change does she get? ☐ p

How much does it cost to buy 1 cabbage and 1 carrot? ☐ p